# One million to
# STOP THE TRAFFIK

## BY MARK WHEELLER

With an original score by Dave Jones.

A Documentary play based on interviews with Phil Lane and Bex Keer from STOP THE TRAFFIK and oral testimony from two books, STOP THE TRAFFIK by Steve Chalke and Stop! She's My Daughter (From the chapter entitled 'Mary's Story: What Price Justice?') © Christine Miles, 2007, a CROP publication (Coalition for the Removal of Pimping).

# One million to STOP THE TRAFFIK by Mark Wheeller

**One Million to STOP THE TRAFFIK script acknowledgements:**

**Phil Lane and Bex Keer whose words have provided the backbone of this play.**

Veronica's story - Stop the Traffik: People shouldn't be bought and sold: The Crime That Shames Us All – Steve Chalke. Lion Hudson Plc.

Cojo's story - stories from the Ivory Coast owned by the International Labor Rights Foundation.

Kiri's story - developed from an amalgam of trafficked peoples experiences by Bex Keer.

Jess from England is taken from **Stop! She's My Daughter** (Mary's Story: What Price Justice? chapter) © Christine Miles, 2007, a CROP (Coalition for the Removal of Pimping) publication.

**Author's Acknowledgements:**

Rachael, Ollie and Daisy, my family, who have to put up with my absence from home due to OYT enthusiasms. STOP THE TRAFFIK for their ongoing support. Sam Allen Turner and her husband Richard of Avalon Entertainment Limited whose generous support allowed Oasis Youth Theatre to purchase the set and assisted us with raising the funds to get to Scotland to perform in the British Final. Sam (ne Phillips) was a former OYT member. I'd like to thank her for remembering us! Carley Wilson: For admin support and a stream of ideas throughout the rehearsal period. Kirsty Housely for her creative ideas during our one day workshop. Ian Golding, Principal, Oasis Academy Lord's Hill, for caring and active support throughout the development of this project. Kate Bulpit: Business Development Director Oasis Academy Lord's Hill whose tireless work fundraising allowed OYT to achieve as they did without worries. John Cunningham: Central Oasis Press Team for PR work well beyond the call of duty. Steve Chalke and all at Oasis Community Learning for support and much enthusiasm. The cast of the original production and those who were part of the development team 2009/10. Evie, Dawn & Lynda from dbda who are always so willing to consider my plays for publication. Sophie Gorell Barnes and all at MBA for their continued support and belief.

# Foreword

Human trafficking is a crime that shames us all. It constitutes a severe human rights violation and a form of violence against its victims. It happens in Africa, America, Asia, and Europe. It affects women, children and men all around the world. It is driven by gender inequality, the absence of equal opportunity, economic disparities, corruption, and the failure of States to protect and provide for their citizens. It is fueled by the demand for commercial sex and cheap construction, manufacturing, agricultural and domestic labour.

But what does human trafficking mean? According to the United Nations Protocol to Prevent, Suppress and Punish Trafficking in Persons, Especially Women and Children, Trafficking in persons shall mean

- **[action:]** the recruitment, transportation, transfer, harbouring, or receipt of persons

- **[means:]** by means of the threat or use of force, coercion, abduction, fraud, deception, abuse of power or vulnerability, or giving payments or benefits to a person in control of the victim

- **[purpose:]** for the purpose of exploitation, which includes exploiting the prostitution of others, sexual exploitation, forced labour, slavery or similar practices, and the removal of organs.

In his new and ground breaking play 'One Million to STOP THE TRAFFIK', the author Mark Wheeller addresses all of the above in a captivating manner. By telling the story of the civil society organization STOP THE TRAFFIK, Mark Wheeller confronts spectators with the horror of human trafficking and equips them with the knowledge to fight it.

Performing arts are a powerful means to raise awareness about human trafficking. Conveyed by youth, the message is even stronger. The United Nations Global Initiative to Fight Human Trafficking (UN.GIFT), an alliance of organizations in the fight against trafficking, believes that youth has a crucial role in facing this global challenge. It is therefore that UN.GIFT and STOP THE TRAFFIK have worked together to empower young people in the past and will continue to do so in the future.

UN.GIFT is honored to feature in 'One Million to STOP THE TRAFFIK' and is grateful to all the young men and women who support the fight against human trafficking.

**Sandra Kozeschnik**
UN.GIFT Civil Society Focal Point

**UN.GIFT**
Global Initiative to Fight Human Trafficking

# Foreword

I had no idea that people in this day and age are still being bought and sold… let alone in such vast numbers. I had no idea until I witnessed a short yet powerful presentation by STOP THE TRAFFIK (STT) in 2008. This campaigning organisation had been established by the sponsors of our new Academy (Oasis) which had opened that year. STT's presentation was aiming to elicit ideas from the Academy staff for new projects. I had an idea: an awareness raising documentary play.

I spoke to the presentation team and they allowed me to progress it. I think they imagined a much smaller project than I had in mind. I was determined for them to see the quality of our work as early as possible, so asked them to send us some testimonies which I could give to Oasis Youth Theatre (OYT) to develop. They kindly accepted my invitation to meet the cast and see these mini performances later that month.

By the time the testimony arrived I had assembled a group who quickly became excited by the potential of this play. We decided that we would have an eighteen month period to develop it with performances due in March 2010. It seemed a long way off and demanded much maturity from the cast with no instant performance possibilities.

The group was made up of 14 old and new OYT members aged between 14 and 23. I purposely involved more people than I imagined would end up in the final production. The older ones were all keen to break new ground with the production and use a strong more physical style of presentation than in previous Wheeller productions.

When I handed out the testimony (unaltered to small sub groups) two groups independently decided to present the material using virtually no words. One of these scenes became the basis for what became our opening scene (Veronica's story) and set a style that we would use throughout. The three devisor/performers were all incredible hip-hop dancers (one was my son Charlie!). They cleverly and subtly incorporated "popping" and "waving" into their performance which I loved as soon as I saw it. This led us to our portrayal of the threat of the predators in the final production. We knew these scenes were special and couldn't wait to show Bex from STT. I remember driving her back to the train station afterwards sensing that she was beginning to see what kind of potential our production might have.

I still didn't have a framework in which these stories could exist.
I decided I didn't want to focus on one story because there are
so many different forms of trafficking and I wanted the play to
expose a number of them. I was also determined to use the original
testimony as it was so emotive. What I needed was a "guide" to
tour the audience round the various problems. A visitor from Oasis
Bangladesh came to the Academy and suggested that Phil Lane,
who co-founded STOP THE TRAFFIK would fit the bill perfectly.

A meeting was set up, and following the Christmas break I interviewed
Phil and was able to start writing the script using his testimony.

Around that time I also saw a TV film about the fall of Thatcher...
or the rise of Blair (I can't remember which) portraying the climatic
journey towards a particular number of votes, and another idea
struck me. STOP THE TRAFFIK's determination to obtain one million
signatures could be interwoven with the harrowing testimonies of
those trafficked. Thus a structure was born and would also allow (with
a bit of dramatic license) some light relief in what were to become the
office scenes.

I remember arriving at our first meeting after the Christmas break
with about half the script freshly photocopied. I left some lines
unallocated (an idea I'd seen Mark Ravenhill use in his powerful
ensemble play Pool No Water) which allowed more flexibility in line
allocation with this large cast. Such occasions are always nerve-
wracking for me as I have no idea how my solitary efforts at home
will go down. There was a very positive response and we immediately
set about staging it using an original technique I hoped would offer
maximum opportunity for everyone to have some input. It was simply
for the group to "guess" where I intended them to go on stage at any
given moment. They all had to remain actively involved. If they got
completely stuck, they were allowed to talk which often led to more
complicated ideas being developed.

The people in the office scenes did the same thing with Carley Sefton
who organically took on the role of Assistant Director. At the end
of the evening each group showed their work and benefited from
forthright evaluations. These were sketches of the scenes just to check
that they would work on stage. For the most part they did. I probably
made fewer changes to this script in the rehearsals than any other
I have worked on. From February to July we continued in this manner
knowing that in September rehearsals proper would begin.

# Foreword

We gave a short preview in July of the Veronica scene which is fascinating to look back on now. It can be seen on the dbda DVD WheellerPlays - The Definitive Author's Collection and shows the beginnings of the final scene which eventually had eighteen people in it! This early version was developed when I imagined we would have a much smaller cast. It features only three OYT members. The obvious quality of this certainly served to raise expectations for One Million to STOP THE TRAFFIK as it was now called.

In September I created a new problem. I had met some young people during the year and wanted to introduce them to OYT. However, with fewer dropping out than I had anticipated we started rehearsals with a cast of twenty (it eventually went down to eighteen). This was too many, particularly as smaller casts generally seem to fare better in the Festival we were entering, but we moved forward with the large cast in the blind faith that somehow it would work.

Stupidly, in retrospect, we had failed to note down any of the movements we had developed in the "guess" sessions and, as no one could remember what we had done, effectively we started to stage the play afresh in September. We used the "guess" technique for most of the play (the Jess scene was a notable exception as I wanted to do it very simply a la Missing Dan Nolan and have less people on stage). I was determined to incorporate the hip-hop dancers as puppeteer style predators throughout the play which meant they became central to the action but hardly ever spoke. It was perhaps the most significant idea of the production and I am so pleased we had the talent in our group to pull it off so effectively!

By December we were able to show a complete run through to, amongst other interested parties, Bex from STOP THE TRAFFIK. This was a thrilling evening. The reaction was fantastic even though for some scenes the cast were still working from scripts!

There was another development that evening. Our set designer had already had the idea of using a children's climbing frame. We'd been scouring catalogues to see if we could find something that would fit the bill with little success. Carley invited her set constructor friend (Chip) from the Nuffield Theatre to see the play. At the end I saw he was deep in conversation with the two predators and together they came up with an idea of a custom built steel frame.

The following week I was invited to Costa Coffee in Romsey (nice!) to see 3D designs for the proposed structure. Being perfectly honest I couldn't imagine how we could use this in the play, but the cast had been so excited by the idea that I put my trust in them and commissioned it, spending literally all of the generous donation we had been given by Sam Allen Turner, a former OYT member.

In January the frame arrived and using the basic moves for the production we'd shown to Bex, re-rehearsed everything incorporating the new set. It was soon clear (even to me) what a major force this structure would become in the production. Our predators now perched on, hid in, and swung from the frame. It offered endless possibilities, fantastic use of levels and on some scenes the whole cast fitted inside it as though they were caged animals. The office scene transitions were speeded up significantly by the simple addition of blocks on casters. It transformed what I already believed was a very impressive production.

Costumes were designed and were again simple but highly effective. The ensemble wearing black tee shirts (predators in red) with the STOP THE TRAFFIK hand logo on the front, and on the back, a genius idea from Kat Chivers our costume designer, a line from the script selected by each of the cast.

The next component was the original musical underscore OYT commissioned from ex member Dave Jones which, with a more stable script, lifted each scene to ever increasing emotional heights. Danny Sturrock finally added his imaginative multi media. These are now available from dbda for schools to use in their productions.

Everything was going so well... then in the final month of preparations two cast members unexpectedly dropped out due to unforeseen work opportunities. Fortunately we were able to replace them from the large cast so, although it was time consuming and very frustrating to re-rehearse everything, we did cope. Then, ten days before the first performance... disaster! An overseas organisation who had provided a testimony replied to a message Bex had sent months before, withdrawing their permission for us to use one of the main stories in the play. Bex hoped we would be able to agree changes but could not offer me much reassurance that they would realise the urgency of the situation and speed up their communications.

# Foreword

I decided that the only way out with ten days to go would be to completely replace the scene. I asked Bex to dictate over the phone a story that typified many different cases amalgamated to raise the issues the original story was aiming to raise. Forty-five minutes later I had a new story to adapt written down hastily on whatever paper had come to hand! I spent the rest of the day adapting it for the rehearsal that evening. I went in and revealed the bad news. If we were to put the production on as planned we would have to plot this scene in this three hour rehearsal. It was a nightmare but the crisis pulled us all together and by the end of the evening, which had been stressful at times, we felt we had possibly the most imaginative scene in the play... the Kiri scene.

The premiere was a memorable evening. Phil Lane was there and also Steve Chalke who I had not met. I remember standing at the back of the Oasis Academy Theatre and noticing Steve, who was sat at the front, constantly looking at the programme during the early part of the play. I was concerned it wasn't holding his attention. Afterwards he told me that it was gradually dawning on him that this was a story he recognised and he was using the program to check out that the Phil and Rachel who were on stage were the Phil and Rachel he knew. I imagine at that moment he would also have noticed that he too would soon be represented on stage. What a way to find out!

The reactions were unbelievable. We had a positive review from the local daily newspaper on the first preview, but following the official premiere the Editor of the paper also gave over the main part of his weekly editorial to our production saying:

"Powerful, disturbing, emotional – it was one of the best productions I have seen in a long time, anywhere."

We couldn't believe how well it had been received... well, actually we could... well I could. I knew it would be something very special. Our production went on to win the All England Theatre Festival against around 350 other adult and youth groups. We overcame the idea that only small cast productions can do well at these Festivals... quite an achievement as everyone in the cast has to be outstanding... and they were! We had the time of our lives representing England in Scotland for the British Final. We also had the honour of performing in front of representatives from the United Nations who were flown in specially to see the play when we performed in London! Not even I had imagined that!!!

All of us have been touched by the issues this play raised. We are all aware of what that fair trade logo means now and will make our buying choices with a full understanding. The production has also inspired career choices. One cast member Kathryn, has been inspired by the content in such a way that she is now planning to become a social worker, a role in which she feels she can help people in such dreadful circumstances. Many others are now determined to follow their dreams and have a go at pursuing a role in the Performing Arts/media. It really has been such a powerful process.

Bearing that thought in mind, I'd like to end on a personal note. My own son Charlie has been in OYT for many years and this will (probably) be his final OYT production. He played the bongo's offstage in his first ever production: Missing Dan Nolan. He has always been a committed member of OYT and won awards in each of the Festivals he has participated in, most notably for being the bitch in the dog humping scene in Graham, World's Fastest Blind Runner! In this production he was one of the hip-hop predators (along with Matt Savage) who created such a stir in every performance and also won a couple of awards. I shall miss our journeys together to and from Youth Theatre, but am so rewarded that he is now truly following his dream. He has been accepted on a degree course in Circus Skills in the internationally renowned Circus Space in London. It's a fabulous achievement to get a place on this prestigious degree and I'm very proud that my son is running away to the circus!

Good luck to all of you who work on this production.

# Photographs from the Oasis Youth Theatre production

Veronica (Becky Wiltshire) trapped by predators.

STOP THE TRAFFIK hand - Kathryn Wiltshire.

Charlie Wheeller - STOP THE TRAFFIK.

STOP THE TRAFFIK Oasis Youth Theatre winning the ALL England Theatre Festival.

My Charlie (right) and his hip hop dance mentor Matt after winning the Adjudicators Award at the English final.

# Cast list

**Wednesday 10th March 2010**
**Oasis Academy Theatre Lord's Hill, Southampton.**

| | |
|---|---|
| Phil Lane: | Alex Chalk |
| Steve Chalke: | Michael Mears |
| Alex: | Kathryn Wiltshire |
| Erin: | Kylie Boylett |

## Ensemble

All the remainder of the cast play a variety of roles. I have indicated below the role that most easily distinguishes them in order of appearance.

| | |
|---|---|
| Veronica: | Becky Wiltshire |
| Predators: | Matt Savage & Charlie Wheeller |
| Young Phil: | Callum Watts |
| Rachel: | Natasha Thomas |
| Sunni: | Rob King |
| Whinney: | Hayley Willsher |
| Their father: | Caidyn White |
| Kiri: | Lauren Oakley |
| Raid Leader: | Joey Marks Reilly |
| Cojo: | Kyle Nicholas |
| Mary (Jess's mother): | Gemma Aked Priestley |
| Jess: | Kimberley Cook |

## Back Stage Team

| | |
|---|---|
| Director: | Mark Wheeller |
| Assistant Director: | Carley Sefton-Wilson, |
| Head of Video: | Danny Sturrock |
| Head of Lighting: | Amy Barnett |
| Head of Sound: | Dave Jones |
| Head of Costume: | Kat Chivers |
| Set design/construction: | Charles "Chip" Mead from Laura Swale's original idea |
| Stage manager: | James Jones |
| OYT Admil: | Chris Gilfoy and Claire Pybus |
| Lighting operation: | Dan Phillips |
| Poster Design: | Danny Sturrock |

*Although the play is divided into sections, it should be performed seamlessly with no blackouts.*

**N.B. Every opportunity should be taken to animate the scenes. The performing group should avoid the scenes becoming stationary talking heads.**

*The unallocated lines should be allocated by the performing group/ director as suits each presentation. The allocated lines in brackets provide a guide, but should not be viewed as prescriptive. The words themselves are sacrosanct as they are taken from interviews or original testimony.*

**A note about Music and Media cues: When using the Media, some audio will not be played separately. This will be denoted by an asterisk. When cueing Music and Media, be aware that this is a guide based on the original production and may differ from the timings of other performances.**

**Media 1: Opening Sequence***

**Music 1: Trafficked***

*Lighting fades up to reveal a group of people (male and female) huddled together asleep in the middle of the stage to keep themselves warm. Predators behaving as vulture/vampire like creatures enter from all directions using the "magnetic" power (of the STOP THE TRAFFIK hand with a key emblazoned on the palm) to lure their victims one at a time. In the original production there was a climbing frame like structure on which these predators perched. Throughout the production they take control, puppeteer like, of the actions of the victim characters. They used hip-hop movement to simulate the animalistic nature of the predators and also to morph from one scene/location/character to another.*

*Each of the victims portrayed later in the play are placed in staggered lines across the stage. They stand in silence rocking backwards and forwards awaiting their fate.*

*Each recites their name and age to an imaginary interrogator:*

| | |
|---|---|
| **Veronica:** | Veronica: Maldova, Sixteen. |
| **Kiri:** | Kiri: from so many places in the world... fourteen. |
| **Cojo:** | Cojo |

| (Yao) | ... and Yao |
| Cojo & Yao: | West Africa. Thirteen. |
| Jess: | Jessica: England. Thirteen. |
| Whinney: | Whinney *(pronounced Viyernee)*... nine and my brother |
| Sunni: | Sunni... *(pronounced Sooni)* |
| Sunni & Whinney: | India. |
| All Victims: | Seven. *(Pause)* We're here to work... aren't we? |

*One by one the victims are overpowered by the predators and forced back into a "prison" (where they form a frieze: Captivity) with the exception of the final victim, Veronica, who the predators surround.*

**Music 1/Audio from Media 1 - *Fade Out*.**
**Music 2: Veronica/Warehouse.**

*Media 2: Veronica*

| (Unallocated): | Veronica is 16 years old. She was trafficked to Russia by a Roma family. |

*The performers transform the scene and Veronica mimes hoeing the land. A group enter as farmers involving themselves in agricultural activities eg. carrying a pot, hoeing, harvesting, working with oxen on a yoke, etc. The victims in their frieze behind Veronica make sounds expressing their discomfort which underscore the remainder of this scene which they alternately narrate. Alternatively this can be pre-recorded and played over the music. The vulture/vampire predators do as the narration dictates.*

| (Unallocated): | They promised her work in agriculture but she was forced to beg sitting in an invalid chair. |
| | To make her foot numb, the traffickers injected her. |
| Veronica: | Help... please...<br>Money... please... |

*Commuters pass by expressing a variety of reactions: laughing, ignoring her, on occasions offering her money. The commuters leave. The predators return.*

**(Unallocated):**    They forced her to take drugs and drink alcohol.

**Veronica:**    Drugs... alcohol ... alcohol... drugs... Veronica... sixteen.

*The predators slam her to the ground shouting:*

**Predators:**    Beg

*They chorally beat her (mimes) and ensnare her. When she is settled they make disturbing vocal sounds as they fall into a light sleep.*

**(Unallocated):**    Veronica was exploited for three months earning 400 lei which amounts to about thirty pounds.

### Media 3: Hand Spacer

*(Whispering from those in the Captivity frieze underscores the action)*

**(Unallocated):**    Go! Just go! Get out of here... freedom, run!

*Veronica attempts an escape twice.*

*(Whispering)* Go! Just go! Get out of here... freedom run!

*On the third attempt Veronica evades her captors. She exits. The predators angrily turn to blame each other then exit to search for Veronica, who re-enters and runs into Phil who arrives on stage with a backpack.*

### Music 2 - *Fade Out*

**Phil:**    There you are! You're safe now. Calm!

*One predator enters and seeing she is with Phil backs off frustrated. Veronica and Phil remain alone on stage in a hug showing, for the time being, Veronica is safe.*

*The ensemble move Phil to the DSC and become Phil's interviewers/ mock interrogators.*

Phil… we want to take you…

… right back…

(Beat)

… were there things…

… in your childhood…

… that you felt were…

… unjust...

… that made the pattern…

… of who you have become?

**Phil:** I'll have to think about that. (Beat) I'll have to think about whether I want to tell you as well.

### Media 4: Phils Story

**(Unallocated):** We should take this chance to say Phil Lane is real, and the stories he tells are true.

This is Phil's account of how STOP THE TRAFFIK came to be:

*(Phil as a young boy emerges from the ensemble becoming for this scene Young Phil)*

**Phil:** I was born in Coventry to a very stable, loving family. I was bullied a lot at school between the ages of, I guess when I started school, until I left Coventry at 10. Yes… perhaps that kicked off a hatred of unfairness… a lot of taunting.

**Ensemble:** Lanky!

**Phil:** … being laughed at… *(Everyone points and laughs at Young Phil.)*

**Phil:** I'll tell you something else that happened there as well. It was when people from the Indian sub-continent were starting to come to the

Midlands. There was one little girl from Bangladesh, Japinda, who could hardly speak English and the class mocked her dreadfully. I remember thinking it was so wrong.

**(Unallocated):** But you didn't do anything about it?

What could he do?

Said something!

What would that do?

Get it "out there"!

**Ensemble:** No one listens to little kids.

**Phil:** I remember trying to smile at her, but she wasn't allowed to smile at a boy, and it's like... that feeling of isolation. I must have been about eight years old. Maybe that started it. I really haven't thought about it too much in a linked way. It was just the way the world was, but it did make me feel unhappy.

**(Young Phil)** You **can** make a difference.

**(Unallocated):** When you're eight?

**(Young Phil)** Yes.

**(Unallocated):** Not on your own!

**(Young Phil)** *(To older Phil)* You can and you will!

**Phil:** To cut a long story short after Uni I got a Leaflet offering the opportunity to do some voluntary work overseas, so I found myself working for the Oasis Global Charity and... and met my wife Rachel.

**Ensemble:** Ahhh!

| | |
|---|---|
| Rachel: | I was also on a placement in Mumbai, India. |

**Music 3: Mumbai - *Fade In.***

***Media 5: Mumbai***

| | |
|---|---|
| (Unallocated): | A city of about eighteen million people. |
| Ensemble: | Eighteen million? |
| | ... and thousands of street kids. |
| Rachel: | We set up a drop in centre on Thane *(pronounced Tarner)* railway station. |
| (Unallocated): | It's a medium sized station... about 8 or 9 platforms... |
| | ... people live there begging... |
| | ... doing menial jobs... |
| | .... getting chased… |
| | … by the police... |
| | ... sleeping on the roofs. |
| | Everyone comes into Thane Station. |
| | Kids come in from all over rural India looking for the streets paved with gold in Mumbai... |
| Rachel: | ... they've seen the Hindi movies... |
| Phil: | ... they know that's where it's all made... their parents migrate there in the hope of work... then... |

**Music 3 - Suddenly Stops.**

| | |
|---|---|
| Rachel: | ... the kid gets lost... |

**Media 6: The kid gets lost**

| | |
|---|---|
| Phil & Rachel: | ...or... the parent dies of AIDS. |
| | *Silence* |

### Media 7: Hand Spacer

Rachel:    We got to know those kids and set up a drop-in centre for them.

Phil:    Sounds like a grand name... for what it was.

### Music 4: Drop In Centre - *Fade In.*

(Unallocated):    Two small buildings

With a gap between them

Rachel:    We asked the owner to put a roof on the gap.

Phil:    That was our drop in centre.

Rachel:    We used to get 40 kids packed in there

(Unallocated):    They'd teach literacy,

Numeracy

Life skills,

And games such as:

Ensemble:    Cricket!

Phil:    Giving them room to be kids...

Rachel:...    Cos they spend their whole time trying to earn money,

(Unallocated):    Trying to avoid the police.

... or being beaten up by gangs.

Phil:    Somewhere safe with food and time to enjoy themselves.

Rachel:    They'd take a bath,

Phil:`    "Bath" meaning... bucket of water...

Rachel:    ... and a jug.

Phil:    Then we started a night shelter for about fifteen in the same building...

**Music 4 Fade Out.**

| (Unallocated): | How do you decide who to take? |
| Phil: | There are different levels of street kids: |
| (Unallocated): | Some live in a slum and their parents send them out: |
| | "Go out and beg!" |
| Phil: | But at night they'd go home. |
| (Unallocated): | Or the family is on the street and they go back to their family... |
| | Mum cooks a handful of rice over the fire. |
| Phil: | But there's a hard core who sleep on the station... alone. |
| Rachel: | That's who we were aiming at. |
| Phil: | When we started, the night shelter it was just for boys. |
| Rachel: | Girls were always controlled by somebody... a family member or a pimp or whatever. |
| Phil: | That was when we started to realise about the exploitation of girls. |
| (Unallocated): | There was a growing fear of HIV in early 2000's |

*Media 7: Aids Symbol*

| (Unallocated): | Guys would think |
| | "If you have sex with a virgin its safe." |
| Rachel: | If you have sex with a child and they're active as a prostitute then they're more likely to have contracted the disease because of the physical damage it does to them. |
| Phil: | It was a myth and there were others: |
| (Unallocated): | "If you are HIV positive and you have sex with a virgin you lose the infection." |

| | |
|---|---|
| **Phil:** | So, there was a growing trade with younger and younger girls. |
| **(Unallocated):** | ... and sometime boys... |
| **Rachel:** | ... being forced into prostitution |
| **Ensemble:** | And *(Pause)* there was the sale of children. |
| | *Transition.* |

**Music 5: Sunni and Whinney - *Fade In.***

***Media 8: Sunni and Whinney***

| | |
|---|---|
| **Sunni:** | Brother... |
| **Whinney:** | ... and sister |
| **Sunni:** | Sunni... |
| **Whinney:** | ... and Whinney. Whinney was about nine |
| **Sunni:** | ... and Sunni was about seven. |
| **Both:** | They lived on Platform 1 of Thane station with their... |
| **S & W & Parents:** | ... alcoholic mum and dad |
| **Dad:** | Dad was particularly unpleasant... |
| **Phil & Rachel:** | Sunni & Whinney were just kids |
| **Whinney:** | They used to come along and play... |
| **Sunni:** | ...and be annoying... |
| **Phil:** | You'd give them a meal and they'd complain about it... |
| **Rachel:** | ... you know just the way it should be in some ways. |
| **S & W:** | They were full of play and joy and would march out in umbrage... |
| **Phil & Rachel:** | ... but... one day... they didn't come back. |
| **Sunni:** | Street kids often disappear for one or two weeks. |

| | |
|---|---|
| Whinney: | ... get on the long distance trains... |
| Sunni: | ... sweep the trains or sell things and take the money |
| Phil: | And we'd say... "Where have you been?" |
| S & W: | Goa. |
| Rachel: | We thought they'd done that... |
| Phil: | But after a week or so... when they **didn't** return, we went looking for their parents... |

*Transition*

| | |
|---|---|
| Rachel: | It was early morning... about 10 o'clock. We found their dad... |
| Father: | ... drunk and lying on the floor. |
| Phil: | I speak some Hindi but we also work with great Indian staff who translate for us! |
| Rachel: | For speed we'll lose the translators in this reconstruction! |
| Phil: | "We haven't seen Sunni and Whinney for a week or so... do you know where they are? Have they gone on the trains?" |
| Father: | No. This man offered me fifteen hundred rupees for them. |
| Phil: | That's just £20! |

### Media 9: Sold!

| | |
|---|---|
| Father: | I needed booze so I sold them! |
| Phil: | Do you have any idea where they've gone? |
| Father: | No. |
| Phil: | Don't you care? |
| Father: | Of course I care! The bastard walked off with my kids, but didn't give me my bloody money! |

| | |
|---|---|
| **Rachel:** | How can you say that? |
| **Father:** | They're only children! |
| **Rachel:** | Do you have any idea where they are? |
| **Phil:** | Do the police know? |
| **Rachel:** | The wife was a few metres away and she was kind of glaring at him. |
| **Phil:** | I got the impression she didn't want it to happen but she couldn't stop it. |
| **Rachel:** | She'd lost all kind of influence or self control or whatever because she was constantly drunk. |

**Music 5 - *Fade Out.***

| | |
|---|---|
| **Rachel:** | At that point we went off to find the railway police to see if we could track them down. |
| **Phil:** | I know the parents come over VERY badly in this story and they did an incredibly awful thing but, if you consider what's happened to them in their lives they've totally lacked all the support and the love and the sense of their self worth that we've had, all the way through our lives so… well… they had no standard of care to measure their decisions against. |
| **Rachel:** | If we could have got the money for them they would have thought that was fantastic… or even better… |
| **Mum/Dad:** | … booze! |
| **Phil:** | Oasis now has a good relationship with the police at a city level, but back then there was no mechanism for persuading them to take action. |
| **Whinney:** | What happened to Whinney and Sunni? |
| **Rachel:** | Nobody knows. |

**Music 6: Bass Drone - *Fade In.***

| | |
|---|---|
| Sunni: | Kidnapped and sold into prostitution? |
| Whinney: | Forced labour? |
| Sunni: | Adoption? |
| Phil: | or even *(Pause)* child sacrifice. |
| Rachel: | The story was passed on... |
| Phil: | ... and, as evidence gathered, we realized this was happening on a huge scale. |
| Rachel: | This wasn't just Mumbai it was across India. |
| Phil: | This wasn't just India it was Asia. |
| (Unallocated): | This wasn't just Asia. |
| Ensemble: | It was across the world. |
| Rachel: | It's not 200 years ago. |
| (Unallocated): | Not even fifty years ago. |
| | It was... |
| | ... and is still... |

**Music 6 - *Quick Fade Out*.**

| | |
|---|---|
| Ensemble: | ... happening today.' |
| Phil: | We left India and came to take a position for Oasis in Europe... well I did... |
| Rachel: | Me? I decided to take a back seat as I was busy being a full time mum while Phil started the campaign on human trafficking. |

### Media 10: STT Office

| | |
|---|---|
| **Phil:** | For about a year and a half I lobbied Steve Chalke, *(indicates Steve as he enters. Steve, in contrast to the others, wears a suit with an open necked shirt.)* the founder of the Oasis Global Charity who work with some of the world's poorest and most marginalised communities, to get him to do something on trafficking. *(To Steve)* There's millions of Sunni and Whinney's, but people don't know about it. |
| **Steve:** | Millions? |
| **Phil:** | Between 1 and 2 million every year! |
| **Steve:** | How do you know? |
| **Phil:** | It's like asking for proof of the number of domestic abuse victims. Most are hidden. I can't prove a figure. The US State Department estimate nearly a million people are trafficked across borders each year... kids are trafficked to fight for the military and some... some are even trafficked for their internal organs. Steve... I can't do this on my own. |
| **Steve:** | We need a steering group. |
| **Phil:** | And a team to run all this day to day as well. |
| **Steve:** | *(Erin and Alex enter and are introduced by Steve)* I brought in Erin and Alex as our "team". |
| **Alex:** | We need to raise awareness. |
| **Erin:** | *(Pondering)* We need something big... |
| **Ensemble:** | *(Melodramatically)* Suddenly... there was a knock at the door! |

*(Phil and Steve look at one another, smile as they mutually realise their "clever" theatrical idea of "knocking" on something near to them.)*

| | |
|---|---|
| **Delivery:** | Package. Can you sign here, please? |
| | *(All three rush to sign)* |

| Delivery: | I only need one, it's not a bloody petition. *(Exits)* |
| Phil: | *(Realising)* A petition! |
| Phil & Steve: | A petition! |
| Phil, Steve & Alex: | A petition! |
| Erin | I've got an idea! We could get people to sign something! |
| Phil, Steve & Alex: | A petition! |
| Erin: | Oh! |

**Music 7: Petition - *Fade In.***

| Alex: | They raise awareness..... |
| Steve: | ... gauge the level of interest. |
| Phil: | And those who sign feel they've done something about it. |
| Erin: | An easy way for anyone to take part in the |
| All 4: | "Global fight to STOP THE TRAFFIK". |
| Steve: | We do need a target.... something to aim for... a recognised number... recognised worldwide! |
| Phil: | Like what? |
| Erin: | 100,000? |
| Alex: | *(Laughing)* How will we get 100,000 signatures? |
| Steve: | No.... |
| Phil: | ... it might be possible Steve. |
| Alex: | *(Still laughing incredulously)* Phil, it'd be 25,000 people each how are we gonna do that? |
| Erin: | I'm not sure I could get 25! |

| | |
|---|---|
| Phil: | We can't give up so easily! |

**Music 7 - *Quick Fade Out.***

***Media 11: One Million***

| | |
|---|---|
| Steve: | We need a million! |
| | *Silence* |
| Phil, Erin & Alex: | A million? |
| Steve: | Yes. One million signatures to STOP THE TRAFFIK! The UN can't ignore that! |
| Ensemble: | *(Melodramatically)* A short while later... |

*They all move into a new position on stage to denote the passage of time. Phil and Steve bump into each other and acknowledge the "mistake" by saying each other's names, perhaps shaking hands in recognition of the error. Once in their new positions the scene reconvenes as though nothing has happened.)*

| | |
|---|---|
| Steve: | *(Excitedly)* We now have permission to go to the UN and call on governments to fight trafficking.... but only... if we get one million signatures |
| Phil: | When? |
| Steve: | March 2007... |
| Erin/Alex: | That's less than a year away |
| Steve: | But it's the ideal date isn't it Phil? March 2007... |
| | *(Erin and Alex look at one another baffled)* |
| Phil: | Very clever Steve! 200 years since the end of the British slave trade. *(To Erin and Alex)* Wilberforce and all that? |
| Alex: | But aren't we meant to celebrate freedom on that day? |
| Steve: | Exactly! |

| | |
|---|---|
| Alex: | But you said... |
| Erin: | I don't get it? |
| Steve/Phil: | Irony... |
| Phil: | People say it's stopped... |
| Steve: | ... but it's still rife! |
| Erin/Alex: | Ohhhh... Excellent! Very clever! |
| Phil: | Steve, the question remains... how can we get one million signatures in less than a year? |
| Steve: | We can do it. I know we can. Come on... events... events where lots of people all gather together! |

*A moments thought.*

| | |
|---|---|
| Ensemble: | Glastonbury! |
| Phil: | There'll be loads of people there. |
| Erin: | Yeh... great place to start! |
| Alex: | And I've already got a ticket! |
| Phil: | Perfect! |
| Alex: | Have I just volunteered? |

**Music 8: Glastonbury.**

**Media 12: Glastonbury.**

*A busy scene is established... Glastonbury. Alex approaches a punter.*

| | |
|---|---|
| Alex: | Hi... my names Alex... I'm from Oasis... |
| Punter: | Oasis? |
| Alex: | Yes... Oasis... it's a global charity... |
| Punter: | Ah right... sorry.... thought you meant "Oasis"... See you mate! |

*A punter is having a wee in a corner. Alex approaches him.*

| | |
|---|---|
| Alex: | Hi... I was wondering if I can have a moment of your time... my names Alex... |
| 2nd Punter: | Mine's Mike... |
| Alex: | I'm from STOP THE TRAFFIK.... Basically kids from all over the world are being trafficked into slavery, and we want to get a million signatures... |
| 2nd Punter: | A million? |
| Alex: | ... all I need from you is a signature... and you'll be helping us to STOP THE TRAFFIK |
| 2nd Punter: | Sure. *(He signs)* |
| Alex: | Thanks very much. |

*Scene snaps back to the office.*

**Music 8 - *Fade Out.***

***Media 13: STT Office***

| | |
|---|---|
| Erin: | How many did you get... a thousand? |
| Alex: | No. |
| Phil: | More or less? |
| Erin: | Must be more! |
| Alex: | One hundred and ninety three. Look it was wet and people just wanted to... |
| Phil: | It's a start. |
| Erin: | One hundred and ninety three out of a million? |
| Phil: | At least we don't have to get a million now! |

**Music 9: Internet - *Fade In.***

| | |
|---|---|
| Alex: | I did have a good idea while I was there though. |
| Phil & Erin: | What? |
| Alex: | The internet... this new Facebook thing. There are groups on that for all sorts of mad stuff... thousands sign up... |

Erin:           "I want to have sex on a grand piano"!

**Music 9 - *Sudden Stop.***

Alex/Phil:      What?

Erin:           "I want to have sex on a grand piano." It's a Facebook group. I'm sure if that gets people to sign up then something like One Million people to STOP THE TRAFFIK would do really well.

Phil:           Can you set it up?

Erin:           Easy.

(Ensemble)     A glimmer of hope!

Alex:           The need was ever more desperate...

Phil:           The stories that we heard were beyond belief!

**Media 4: Hand Space**

**(Unallocated):**      Kiri is crying. Her sobbing becomes uncontrollable.

Kiri's mother passed away.

People comfort her...

... and care for her...

... but one or two male figures in her community are not respectful:

*Man 1 approaches and starts to comfort her. They hug.*

**Kiri:**      I miss my mum so much.

**Man 1:**      I miss her too Kiri... you must not cry my sweet... really... she wouldn't want that now would she...

**Music 10: Kiri Drone - *Fade In.***

*The supportive hug becomes intrusive. It is clear he is beginning a journey towards rape. She screams. The scene freezes. He exits.*

**Music 10 - *Fade Out.***

**(Unallocated):**      Kiri is alone...

.. vulnerable.

And with a life changing decision to make.

To stay...

... or to leave.

Her friend tells her of an opportunity she'd be stupid to miss...

**Friend:**      My sister has a job as a seamstress in the capital. You'd earn money Kiri. It would be good for you.

**Kiri:**      I don't want to leave my family.

**Friend:**      It is your only way to escape this hell! Go Kiri... be away from this place.

*(As they say this the ensemble morph into train)*

| | |
|---|---|
| **Kiri:** | She boards a train determined to make something of her life. However, the job does not materialise. Kiri is alone... and vulnerable. |

**Music 11: Kind Man - *Fade In*.**

| | |
|---|---|
| **Man 2:** | She meets a man... *(ensemble simultaneously whisper these three words)* a kind man. |
| **Kiri:** | Kiri feels secure... cherished. |

*The predators suddenly restrain Kiri.*

| | |
|---|---|
| **Man 2:** | *(Furious)* Suddenly the charm disappears. *(Kiri being held allows him to take her passport)* He steals her passport. *(To Kiri)* "If you go to the police they'll put you in prison. If you want to stay here you must pay for the food I give you." |
| **Kiri:** | You know I have no money! |
| **Girls:** | Kiri is sold to a man and moved... |

**Music 11 - *Fade Out*.**

| | |
|---|---|
| **Boys:** | ... to a "house"... |
| **Girls:** | ... where there are other girls... |
| **Ensemble:** | The abuse begins. |

*(Everyone, saying "Yes" lift her off the ground in a horizontal position.)*

| | |
|---|---|
| **(Unallocated):** | They beat her and gave her electric shocks... *(As they say this there is a flash of light and she is lifted as high as possible and returned to a resting place.)* |
| | ... and drugged her. |
| **Kiri:** | Which made her incoherent and compliant. |
| **(Unallocated):** | Some days she is forced to see up to 10 men. |

*(The predators force Kiri to smile by pulling her lips up with their fingers)*

| | |
|---|---|
| **(Unallocated):** | Smile... it'll be over soon. |

| Kiri: | She feels foolish... |
| Girls: | Guilty and ashamed. |
| Kiri: | Isolated in a country where she doesn't speak the language. Kiri loses hope. |
| (Unallocated): | A charity hear rumours of the brothel Kiri works in. They investigate. They plan... |
| (Ensemble): | ...and for once there is no tip off. |

**Music 12 - *Choices*.**

A simple movement sequence indicates an attack on the "establishment".

**Music 12 - *Fade Out*.**

| (Unallocated): | With the help of the police, Kiri and many of the other girls are rescued. |
| Kiri: | I have the chance of a new life. I don't know what it will look like... but I have choices now. I can make good choices. |
| Phil: | And it wasn't only girls... 100s of thousands of boys aged 12 to 16 from across the world are stolen or bought from their parents for a pittance. |

### Media 15: Bus Station

*The ensemble create Sikasso bus station. Phil walks amongst it trying to retain his anonymity and finds a place to wait and watch, once his introduction is complete.*

| | |
|---|---|
| Phil: | In West Africa boys are trafficked to work on cocoa farms. Agents hang around bus stations looking for children, such as Cojo *(indicates him as he enters)*, who are alone or begging for food. |

### Music 13: Cojo - *Fade In.*

| | |
|---|---|
| Cojo: | I left home to earn money for my family. When I got to Sikasso bus station, I... *(He looks around the bus station)* ... I knew no-one. |
| (Unallocated): | What is your name? |
| Cojo: | Cojo Sir. |
| (Unallocated): | Looking for work Cojo? |
| Cojo: | Yes. |
| (Unallocated): | I take you to my brother. |
| Cojo: | He has work? |
| (Unallocated): | Yes. |
| Cojo: | Here? |
| (Unallocated): | The Ivory Coast. |
| Cojo: | I have come to work in Sikasso. My father has died. I must stay near my mother. |
| (Unallocated): | Work here pays badly. Cojo, come with me to Korgho. |
| Cojo: | No. |
| (Unallocated): | You will make lots of money. |
| Cojo: | Thank you sir but I stay here to work. |
| (Unallocated): | My brother pays very well. Will be good for your poor mother? |

| | |
|---|---|
| **Cojo:** | I am too small to go there. |
| **(Unallocated):** | They give you good food. |
| | Chicken... |
| | ... coco cola. |
| **Cojo:** | Sir! I am only ten! |

*Finally the agent drove Cojo to the Ivory Coast.*

**Cojo:**     I was actually excited by how much it would help mother.

*They avoided the border control.*

**Cojo:**     Once across the border I was completely alone. I was taken to a warehouse to sleep. The man who brought me disappeared. There are many children in the warehouse, sometimes more than one hundred. The cocoa planters come and see the warehouse owner. I hear them negotiating my sale.

### Media 16: Cojo Sale

| | |
|---|---|
| **(Unallocated):** | Twelve |
| | Seven |
| | Eleven |
| | Eight |
| | Ten |
| **Ensemble:** | Nine. Sold! |
| **Cojo:** | Then I'm taken to the plantation. One job was to transport the cocoa beans. The bags were taller than me. |

### Media 17: Cocoa Farm

**(Unallocated):**     People placed the bags onto Cojo's head. They were so heavy he often fell down. The farmer beat him til he stood up to lift the bag.

| | |
|---|---|
| Cojo: | We worked from six in the morning to about ten at night. We'd sit on the ground picking up cocoa pods with one hand and, with the other, hacking them open with machete to scoop out the beans. |
| (Unallocated): | Common injury with machete was cutting... ... or accidental amputation *(animate this with a horrifying scream)* of the hands. |

**Media 18: Blood**

| | |
|---|---|
| (Unallocated): | Open wounds expose the boys to HIV. Applying pesticides without the necessary protective equipment leads to horrific skin burns and respiratory damage... |
| (Ensemble) | These can be fatal. |
| Cojo: | If we refuse to work the plantation owners bring razors and slice our feet. |
| (Unallocated): | They put salt in the wounds. |
| Phil: | The children have no communication with anyone. |
| Cojo: | One boy I knew, Yao, tried to escape. |

**Media 19: Fields**

| | |
|---|---|
| Phil: | The plantations are isolated... in the middle of forest. There are no roads out... just fields everywhere. |
| (Yao) | They tied him to a papaya tree. They beat him. They broke his arm. |

**Music 13 - *Fade Out.***

| | |
|---|---|
| Phil: | The pleasure that people from various nations around the world derive from chocolate could be at the expense of children trafficked and enslaved to harvest cocoa beans. |
| Phil: | Constantly hearing stories like these spurred us on... but after a while the Facebook signatures plateau'd... |

**Music 14: Plateau - *Fade In.***

***Media 20: STT Office***

| | |
|---|---|
| Erin: | At about 45,000 |
| Phil: | It seemed like... well... we'd tried everything. |
| Alex: | A million is a such a big number. |
| Erin: | Yes, do you know how long it takes to count to a million? *(Alex and Phil look at one another perplexed)* Twenty three days! |
| Alex: | Why would you know that? |
| Erin: | It's in one of my kid's books... twenty three days! Just think how long it'll take to get a million signatures... and we've only got 203 days now... I worked it out. |
| Phil: | We were really struggling. *(Steve appears unseen by Phil, Erin and Alex.)* |
| Alex: | There's no way we can do this. |
| Erin: | Can it be less than a million? |
| Steve: | *(Moving into the room)* One million is the number that opens the door! We can only present our petition at the UN if we get One million signatures! |
| Phil: | It's difficult to get that level of interest... and getting signatures from undemocratic countries... Steve, these people don't want to draw attention to themselves. |
| Steve: | In this office there's always been a crazy optimism that we will find a solution. I don't want that to change. There's a million grains in a cup of salt. A cupful of signatures? We can do that!!! |
| Phil: | There's another problem. Middle class Europeans seem to think... well... |

Steve:            ... this is all so far away?

Phil:             Yeh.

Steve:            We have to change that perception.

**Music 14 - Fade Out.**

Phil:             Because it isn't.

Ensemble:         It's right on our doorstep.

***Media 21: Jessica***

| | |
|---|---|
| Phil: | Mary Rogers' * 13-year-old daughter was groomed and sexually exploited by a group of men. |
| Jess: | Jess was born with a rare skeletal disorder that affects bone development. |
| Mary: | As she got older, it became more noticeable that one arm was shorter. |
| Jess: | I feel ugly Mum. No lad I like will fancy me! |
| Mary: | She wouldn't go out without a jacket, even if it was scorching, so, I was really proud of her when she became a majorette. One of my proudest moments was when her team won first prize at a holiday camp. She couldn't have looked any happier. |
| | Jess was a normal teenager in every other way; we had no problems at school. At weekends she went out with her friends, but was always in on time. Once or twice I found out she'd had a drop of cider or something, and grounded her for a couple of nights, but you expect that. |
| | One Friday night in July 2005 however, she didn't come home. |
| Jess: | See you Mum. |
| | *(They give each other an "insignificant" kiss goodbye. Jess Exits)* |

**Music 15: Bass Drone - *Fade In.***

| | |
|---|---|
| Mary: | 10pm came and went. At 11.30pm I rang round her friends, then the police. I rang my ex-husband too, and we went out to look for her. That was the worst night of my life. We searched the next day too. Then the police called. |

* Mary Rogers story is taken from Stop! She's My Daughter - chapter entitled Mary's Story: What Price Justice © Christine Miles

**Music 15 - *Fade Out.***

(Unallocated):    "Jessica has been found, with a friend, Gemma"

Gemma:    Gemma was in foster care.

Mary:    What I didn't know was Gemma was being groomed by a network of men operating across towns in England.
Over the next few months life became a nightmare. She wasn't washing and had... she had bruises and... love bites... all over.
I didn't know her anymore.
The worst thing for a parent is not being able to control or protect your own daughter. How do you sleep when your 13 year-old is out on the streets somewhere? You question yourself:
'Is it something I've done? Have I treated her different to my other children?'
But then the police told me how the grooming process works.

**Music 16: Lads - *Fade In.***

**Media 22: *Fast Cars***

(Unallocated):    These lads have fast cars...

They're young...

... and good looking.

They get the girls into their cars by offering them vodka...

... some loud music

... and a bit of a drive.

Gemma :    The girls may say 'no' one night

Jess:    ... but another night they might have had a bit of cider

Jess/Gemma:    and say:

(Unallocated):    'Yes':

| | |
|---|---|
| **Gemma/Jess:** | That's when it starts. |
| **(Unallocated):** | They get alcohol… |
| | … and presents… |
| **Jess/Gemma:** | *(excited)*… especially mobile phones. |
| **(Unallocated):** | They call the girls |
| | 'Princess' |
| **Jess/Gemma:** | …and make them feel special. |
| **(Unallocated):** | Then a few spliffs… |
| | … and before they know it… |
| | … they pass the girls on to older men. |
| | The older men introduce the girls to… |
| | … Class A drugs. |
| | The girls become reliant on the men… |
| | … and the drugs. |
| | The men are seen to be fun… |
| | … so they're the good ones |
| | … and the family are bad. |
| **Mary:** | The parents are made to look like they just want to keep the girl in, and make her life miserable. But it becomes more sinister because then it's payback time. |

### Media 23: Jessica Backdrop

*(The girls are violently thrown to the floor)*

| | |
|---|---|
| **(Unallocated):** | Drugs cost…. Drugs cost money |

*(They hit the girls)*

| | |
|---|---|
| **Jess/Gemma:** | They send the girls to pinch things. |
| | The girls are passed around… |
| | … the men might threaten to… |

| | |
|---|---|
| Gemma: | … smash up my house |
| Jess: | … and rape my mum |

**Music 16 - *Fade Out*.**

| | |
|---|---|
| Mary: | They rule. There is… |
| Ensemble: | … no escape. |

Mary:   At first I didn't want anyone to know. I felt ashamed that she was involved, but after the police had been here so often, I realised it wasn't about shame. It was about a young girl, a child, being exploited. I wanted these men caught, locked up. The law seemed powerless to protect my daughter.
I called social services. I begged for help. They put Jess in a foster home round the corner. Every night I'd get a text from her foster carer saying she wasn't home. Again, it was me out looking for her, so I asked for her to be moved out of county. I went to my local MP.
"If you don't I fear I'll find her dead in a gutter? I want something done! If you don't, I'll go to the papers!"
Within weeks, social services found her a therapeutic foster care place out of county.
I couldn't have asked for a better placement, but after a week and a half two men abducted her.

**Music 17: Innocence - *Fade In*.**

She was missing for a couple of days before she was found… with Gemma. Jess alleged she was hit with an iron bar by one man and chose to testify.
Two men were charged with supplying a Class A drug, detaining a child without lawful authority, and having sex with a child under the age of 16.

People think things like this only happen to 'bad' families, but it can happen to anybody. These

girls are victims of criminal acts: you are not to blame and nor are they. It's these men who are to blame. They've taken her innocence.
I am scared what my actions will be if these men get let off. I will go off my head. She's got problems in her head – big ones... recently threats of suicide...

**Music 17 - *Fade Out.***

Jess:     Mum, you don't know what it's like. I don't want to be here.

Mary:     I was frightened she would do something.

***Media 24: Childhood***

Jess:     (*Underscores the following words by singing:*)
Boys and girls come out to play,
The moon does shine as bright as day;
Come with a hoop, and come with a call,
Come with a good will or not at all.
Loose your supper, and loose your sleep,
Come to your playfellows in the street;
Up the ladder and down the wall.
A halfpenny loaf will serve us all.

Mary:     She was singing nursery rhymes and getting all the stuff out from when she was little. She had her majorettes medal round her neck.

***Media 25: Jessica Backdrop***

Jess:     I want to die with this medal on. It was my favourite time!

(Unallocated):     There are loopholes in the law.

          Sex with someone under 16 is illegal.

          But prosecution relies on the testimony of the child.

          In practice when a child is over 13 she has to testify.

          The men know that.

They groom the girls to have sex with them as they turn 13.

The girls are too frightened to give evidence...

... or don't always fully understand that they were groomed...

... and that these men...

... were not real boyfriends.

*(The singing stops suddenly as Mary breaks into her speech.)*

**Mary:** I want to put a stop to this, that's why I'm speaking out. No-one warned me that these lads drive round in their posh cars playing loud music grooming girls, and I didn't warn my daughter. I want other parents to be aware.

**Phil:** The two men, aged 31 and 47 who abducted Jessica pleaded guilty to all charges.

**Mary:** They were sentenced to imprisonment of 5 years and 8 months each but would probably be released after only two years.

**Jess:** With dependency issues remaining, Jessica remains a vulnerable target.

| | |
|---|---|
| Phil: | Middle class western people were signing via Facebook and our petitions, but we had to do much more than that! |

***Media 26: Ticking Office***

**Music 18: Clock -** *Fade In.*

| | |
|---|---|
| Phil: | We only have three months left... |
| Erin: | 84 days to be precise Phil... |
| Phil: | ... and another 700,000 signatures to get. We're not even half way yet! |
| Alex: | *(Enters excitedly)* "Delirious?" have just called.... |
| Phil: | ... a rock band. They did a gig in Mumbai... was just an idea... to get some interest from other parts of the world. |
| Alex: | Shot in the dark eh Phil? |
| Phil: | Worth a try. |
| Alex: | Certainly was. |
| Phil: | What's happened? |
| Alex: | 200,000 people signed... |
| Erin: | 200,000? |
| Alex: | Yes! *(Celebration)* That's not all. They played Columbia yesterday night and did the same thing! 400,000 signatures! |
| Erin & Phil: | Yes! |
| Phil: | In the remaining 83 days *(Erin smiles)* we came within sight of our target. We collected petitions from every continent through: |
| Alex: | Signed postcards; |
| Erin: | Thumb prints; |
| Phil: | Freedom walls; |
| Alex: | Website sign ups; |

| | |
|---|---|
| Phil: | Football events; |
| Alex: | Yeh, a Watford player had been trafficked so they asked fans to text in. |
| Phil: | With just over 100,000 signatures to get and only… *(Looks at Erin)* |
| Erin: | … eight days Phil. |
| Phil: | Eight days to go… we got in touch with a Nigerian church network. We were right up against our deadline. |
| Erin: | Our hearts were pounding. |
| Phil: | This was a mass gathering in a country where trafficking is… well prolific! |
| Alex: | We waited for their response. |
| Phil: | … and waited… |
| Erin: | … waited… |
| Alex: | … waited… |
| Erin: | 3 days to go! |
| Ensemble:… | Waited… |
| Phil: | … for news. |

**Music 18 - Fade Out.**

| | |
|---|---|
| Steve: | Guys… we have news. |

***Media 26: STT Office***

| | |
|---|---|
| Phil, Erin & Alex: | Well? |
| Steve: | I think you should sit down. |
| Erin: | Just tell us! |
| Steve: | You need to sit down. |
| Phil: | Have they said no? If they say no we're done! There's nothing else to do… no one else we can go to! |

| | |
|---|---|
| Steve: | They said yes! |
| Phil, Erin & Alex: | What? |
| Steve: | They're all signing. |

**Music 19: Your Community - *Fade In.***

| | |
|---|---|
| Phil: | In the end we had one and a half million signatures! |
| Erin: | And a platform to deliver them at GIFT, the first UN global initiative to fight trafficking |
| Steve: | The UN recognised that we at STOP THE TRAFFIK have relationships with people around the world... |
| Erin: | Steve spoke powerfully. |
| Phil: | They gave him the position of UN Special Advisor on Community Action Against Trafficking. |
| Alex: | We hadn't expected that! |
| Erin: | Everyone who signed made a difference… |
| Phil: | And will continue to. |
| Alex: | When people act things change. |
| (Cast enter) | |
| (Unallocated): | STOP THE TRAFFIK engage with communities |
| | … and professionals... |
| | … to make it harder to traffick... |
| | Harder to hide and exploit people. |
| Kiri: | Kiri's story is evidence of this. |
| Veronica: | And Veronica's. |
| Jessica: | And Jessica's. |
| Phil: | Let's hope it's still possible to rescue... |
| Sunni: | Sunni, |

# Section 9

| | |
|---|---|
| Whinney: | ... and Whinney. |
| Cojo: | Remember Cojo... |
| (Yao) | ... and his friend Yao? |
| (Unallocated): | Always buy fair trade... |
| Cojo: | If we don't... we are buying something Cojo and his friends suffered to make. |
| (Unallocated): | Trafficking starts in the community and ends in the community... |
| Ensemble: | ... our community. |
| | In 2009, when this play was created... |
| | ... STOP THE TRAFFIK campaigned relentlessly... |
| | ... to get seven major companies to agree... |
| | ... to make certain chocolate bars traffic free. |

**Music 19 - *Fade Out.***

| | |
|---|---|
| Phil: | Our 2009 Christmas campaign on Nestlé will give you an idea of how we work. |

**Music 20: Christmas - *Fade In.***

***Media 28: Nestlé***

*The ensemble organise themselves into two groups on opposite sides of the stage. A STOP THE TRAFFIK (STT) group and a Nestlé group.*

| | |
|---|---|
| (Unallocated): | Now it's time to give Nestlé a Christmas they'll never forget. |
| | Wrap up your favourite fair trade chocolate bar... |
| | ... and send it to Nestlé with a lovely Christmas message. |

*The STT group hurl (mimed) chocolate bars at the Nestlé group with added vocal sound effects. The Nestlé group chorally react as though the chocolate bar has hit them on the head. They freeze.*

| | |
|---|---|
| (Unallocated): | We're wrapping up fair trade chocolate for Christmas presents… |
| STT: | … shame it's not yours. |
| (Unallocated): | Wishing you a happy Christmas and a happy new Year… |
| Erin, Alex Phil, & Steve: | Now give children in the Ivory Coast a Happy Christmas… |
| STT: | … by producing fair trade chocolate. |

*The Nestlé group respond by putting their hands to their chin in pensive manner and saying.*

| | |
|---|---|
| Nestlé: | Mmmmmmm? *(Realising the error of their ways they change their gesture with the following word)* Ahhhhh! |
| Phil: | Nestlé surrendered after only a few weeks of this campaign, announcing the four finger Kit Kat would become fair trade from January 2010. *(Cast cheer, Phil, Steve, Erin and Alex gently stop them from cheering)* No. Only the four finger bar. We have more work to do on them and other companies. |
| Phil: | Everything we do… |
| Ensemble: | … will make a difference… |
| Alex: | The creation of this play is an example of the kind of thing STOP THE TRAFFIK does to raise awareness. |
| Phil: | If people don't know what trafficking is they'll never recognise it. |
| Erin: | Showing this play raises awareness. |
| Phil: | When it was first suggested I wondered what the ending would be. |
| Steve: | It soon became obvious… |
| Alex: | These simple words… |

## Media 29: STOP THE TRAFFIK*

**Phil, Alex
Erin & Steve:**    People should not be bought and sold.

**Ensemble:**    *(With palms - and emblazoned key logo - facing the audience.)*

STOP…

## Music 21: STOP THE TRAFFIK.*

… THE TRAFFIK

**The End**

# STOP THE TRAFFIK,
## PEOPLE SHOULDN'T BE BOUGHT & SOLD

## PEOPLE SHOULDN'T BE BOUGHT AND SOLD
### but what can you do?

- **TRAFFICKING IS...** to be deceived or taken against your will, bought, sold and exploited in places like the sex industry, sweat shops, factories, circuses, for sacrificial worship, body parts, forced begging, cannabis cultivation or domestic servitude.

- **TRAFFICKING IS...** where family members, friends or even strangers decieve or coerce parents into releasing or selling their children for as little as $20.

- **TRAFFICKING IS...** where men, women and children are taken across borders, moved within the same country or from one part of a city to another. ON average, one person one person is trafficked across a borders every minute and a child is trafficked within and between countries every 30 seconds.

- **TRAFFICKING IS...** here victims usually suffer repeated physical abuse, fear, torture and threats to themselves and their families. The same person can be sold and resold many times.

- **STOP THE TRAFFIK** is a growing global movement working through individuals, organisations and communities to stop the trafficking of people.

- **STOP THE TRAFFIK** believes trafficking can only be stopped through community awareness and action.

- **STOP THE TRAFFIK** exists to provide resources so anyone and everyone can be part of the fight to prevent trafficking, protect the vulnerable and prosecute the traffickers.

### CHOCOLATE

Over a third of the world's chocolate comes from cocoa plantations in Cote d'Ivoire, West Africa.

Thousands of children are trafficked onto these plantations and forced to harvest the beans to make our favourite comfort food. STOP THE TRAFFIK demand the chocolate industry provide traffik free chocolate.

A few big chocolate companies have started making one or two Traffik Free bars, but it is not enough! Help keep the pressure on by

- buying fair trade chocolate

- hosting a chocolate fondue party

- writing a letter to Neslté

**www.stopthetrafffik.org/ chocolate**

## START FREEDOM

In partnership with the United Nations and the Serious Organised Crime Agency, this multi-lingual campaign is for schools and young people to become aware of issues surrounding human trafficking, how it affects their life and what they can do to combat it.

- get your teachers/local schools/ youth groups involved!

**www.startfreedom**

## Become an ACTIVE COMMUNITY against TRAFFICKING (ACT)

ACT is based on the idea that trafficking starts in a community and can be stopped by a community.

Students around the world are among the most active when it comes to campaigning and social justice issues - exactly the kind of people to run a campaign to fight human trafficking!

ACT resources help mobilise and inspire you to:

- find out what is happening in your area

- raise awareness about different types of trafficking

- become a voice for those hidden or vulnerable

- campaign and lobby for local, national and international change

- fundraise and organise show stopping stunts

Find out more online:
**www.stopthetraffik.org/act**

## FREEDOM TICKET FOR LIFE

Most trafficking victims are girls or women. They are more vulnerable because in many countries, they don't have equal access to education, training and work. Education and training means choice. Choice means freedom.

STOP THE TRAFFIK are supporting four organisations in trafficking hotspots, helping girls into education and / or helping survivors. Fundraise with us by running, walking, crawling or racing on wheels to give a vulnerable girl her freedom ticket for life. Everything you need to know can be found here
**www.freedomticketforlife.org**

**Sign up, get your school sweaty!**

## One Million to STOP THE TRAFFIK DVD
## by Mark Wheeller

One million to STOP THE TRAFFIK tells true stories of people who are trafficked. Sunni and Whinney, just 6 and 8 years old, were sold by their parents; their story inspired the formation of the campaign team STOP THE TRAFFIK. 'People should not be bought and sold' became the campaign's mantra. One Million to STOP THE TRAFFIK tells the true story of their determined quest to get 1,000,000 signatures enabling them to go to the United Nations and call on governments to fight human trafficking.

As the play is made up of short episodes it is possible to select extracts for examination performances.

OYT's award winning production, which won the All England Theatre Festival Final where they competed against more than 300 other groups in the country, features on the professionally filmed DVD.

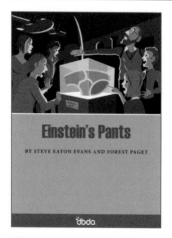

## Einstein's Pants
## by Steve Eaton Evans and Forest Paget

In the last century temperatures have risen by 0.5°C, the oceans by 8 inches and rainfall by 1%. It was against this background that an environmental play was commissioned by Dorset County Council. The result was Einstein's Pants, written by Steve Eaton Evans and Forest Paget.

What if $E=MC^2$ was not Einstein's greatest theorem? What if he wrote another one that was even more important - and he only wrote it down once... in a secret place where no one would think to look?

Barney is just an ordinary teenager but, with the help of his new friend Alice, he uncovers the secret of... Einstein's Pants.

ISBN 978 1 902843 27 8

*Cast:* 3f & 2m with doubling, or 6f, 3m & 16
*Duration:* 55 minutes approx.
**KS 3 to adult**

'**This is an effective and powerful way to communicate important messages**'
*Dave Goddard, Director Dorset LEA*

'Inspired... Imaginative and witty'
*The Independent*

# Other plays published by **dbda**

**Wheellerplays**
The Definitive Author's Collection

BY MARK WHEELLER

dbda

ISBN 978 1 902843 32 2

**Duration:** Scenes are between 5 and 15 minutes long.
**Suitable for KS 3,4 and beyond.**

**A CD of the original music tracks is included with the DVD**

## Wheellerplays: The Definitive Author's Collection - Script and DVD by Mark Wheeller

These scenes were selected by Mark as he uses them regularly on courses. People often refer to his scripts as having a "devised feel". The reason for this is simple. These scripts were born out of an educational, rather than a theatrical background. Consequently these scenes encourage students to be imaginative in their presentations.

There are opportunities to stage naturalistic conversations, stylised arguments and epic scenes (a car crash and an arson attack). There are monologues using oral testimony and a stylised scene from one of his early musicals which uses a large cast most imaginatively.

Each extract is preceded by an introduction from Mark: **Too Much Punch For Judy, No Place for a Girl, Chunnel of Love, Legal Weapon II, Arson About, Missing Dan Nolan, The Gate Escape, Kill Jill, Driven To Distraction, One Million to STOP THE TRAFFIK**

The DVD shows versions of each of these scenes by Mark's award winning (All England Theatre Festival Champions 2010) Oasis Youth Theatre from the Oasis Academy Lord's Hill in Southampton. Mark is particularly impressed by a group who created a vibrant version of the crash scene from Too Much Punch for Judy which he says "beats any version I have seen or directed!" The Kill Jill scene featuring hip hop body scenery directed by NYT & OYT member Matt Savage is another to admire.

'For more than twenty years OYT has produced interesting, sometimes challenging work, to growing acclaim. As befits an educational tool, the proceedings begin with a short exercise illustrating perfectly the dramatic style which OYT has made its own and underpins many productions involved... Even a piece on human trafficking is compelling and emotionally engaging. The young players are impressive in their confidence and versatility... bravado performances... a perfect showcase.'

*Karen Robson Southern Evening Echo (on the original live performances)*

**ISBN 978 1 902843 30 8**

**Cast:** *flexible. Min. 2-3m/2f, with doubling, max. up to 30, with chorus*
**Duration:** *60 minutes approx*
*KS 3 & 4*

## CRASH
## by Andrew Fusek Peters and Polly Peters

Both a play and a story told in verse, Crash weaves together different voices into a powerful drama in which the best and the worst happens. This accessible text has direct appeal to upper KS3 and KS4 and explores many issues around road safety and consequences.

Crash can be used for full-length performance by TIE companies, schools or youth theatres. Alternatively, individual scenes/monologues can be explored practically as stand alone pieces during drama lessons or youth theatre sessions or for examinations. Sections can be used for discussion in English and in PHSE/Citizenship.

Crash offers a framework for developing the individual and ensemble-based performance skills explored by students for course requirements.

'The authors have imagined a story behind a bunch of flowers left at the scene of a road accident, and they have done so with force, tenderness, eloquence and economy.'
*TES.*

'Original to its core in both the telling and the tale - it should be read and discussed in classrooms and common rooms up and down the land.'
*TES. Jo Klace, director of the National Literacy Association*

'Remarkably accessible… from tender and funny to morally thoughtful.'
*The Bookseller*

'The pace is fast, the emotions raw and the narrative voices ring true.'
*The School Librarian*

'This heart-wrenching tale of road abuse is brought vividly alive. It is a rich, thought provoking read'
*Northern Echo*

# Other plays published by **dbda**

ISBN 978 1 902843 20 9

**Cast:** *11+ (3m, 3f & 5 m or f)*
*Suitable for GCSE with doubling*
*(2m, 2f & 1 m or f)*
**Duration:** *50 minutes approx.*
**Suitable for:** *ages 13+ or*
*adults!*

*Commissioned and*
*premiered by The*
*Birmingham Rep Theatre*

## KILL JILL
## by Mark Wheeller

Big Brother meets Kill Bill meets Jack (of Beanstalk fame) meets Tony Martin... Mix these together to create *Kill Jill!* This brand new play by Mark Wheeller explores the topical issues of homeowners defending themselves, and asks "How far can Reality TV be allowed to go?"

Jill is the latest victim of Reality Lottery, a futuristic form of National Service to entertainment. She accompanies Jack as he (again) robs George, who lies in wait armed with a shotgun. The Reality Lottery camera operators are filming everything... but should they intervene? The ending is suitably Tarantinoesque!

*Kill Jill!* raises issues of rights and responsibilities. It is a play full of interesting techniques that will delight Drama teachers and students, and will thrill those exploring Citizenship issues through imaginative and entertaining Theatre productions.

'Kill Jill is a very fizzy ride! What a great script! The playfulness with style and wide range of reference points with an 'anytime, anyplace, anywhere' theatrical freedom... the banter goes to some strange places too - perhaps a Python influence? The build up of tension in the visit to George's castle puts the end of the play in firm thriller territory! Wonderful stuff!!!!!'

*Paul Mills, Head of Drama,*
*Westgate School, Winchester*

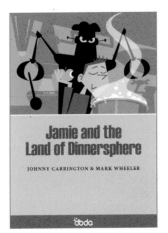

**Jamie and the**
**Land of Dinnersphere**

JOHNNY CARRINGTON & MARK WHEELER

dbda

ISBN 978 1 902843 25 4

*Cast:* 2m and 2f with doubling or 3m, 1f and 5 or 6m/f. Suitable for use as a TIE production in the new vocational courses for ages 13+ (or as a performance piece in Primary schools)
*Duration:* 35 minutes (55 minutes with the workshop)

## Jamie and the Land of Dinnersphere
## (a Healthy school dinners play)
## by Johnny Carrington & Mark Wheeller

Jamie Jamjar loves healthy food. He has seen how a poor diet can mess you up... just by looking at his sister... Lazy Lillian! Jamie is shocked when his school tries out the new Robot Dudes (fast food servants) who replace the friendly dinner ladies. Jamie then discovers his own father invented them!

Can it get any worse? Yes it can!

Jamie is transported to Dinnersphere (in another of his father's inventions, a Story Rocket) where Jamie discovers the nefarious Dinnerwitch, busy planning world domination through putrid school dinners! Together with three friends, Bo, Agor and another - a member of the Primary School audience - they confront and defeat the Dinnerwitch!

Jamie provides an opportunity for secondary school students to present an interactive Theatre In Education play with all the joys of the audience being a key part of the final performance. It is expected to become a staple part of the new vocational courses where there are, at the moment, few plays which will fit the specification so well!

The text includes an innovative interactive workshop written by Adrian New (Stopwatch Theatre) which can be led by the secondary students.

SCHOOL
FOOD TRUST
Eat Better Do Better

# Other plays published by **dbda**

ISBN 978 1 902843 05 6

**Cast:** *3f, 3m & 6 or 2m & 2f with doubling*
**Duration:** *45 minutes approx.*
**Suitable for:** *ages 14+*

## Too Much Punch For Judy
## by Mark Wheeller

May 20th 1983... a lonely road near Epping... a car comes off the road and hits a bridge. The scaffolding construction slices through the car. The driver, Judy, escapes unhurt, but the passenger, her sister, Joanna is killed outright. Joanna and Judy were on their way home from an aerobics session followed by a trip to the local Wine Bar. They had both been drinking.

This tragic incident was dramatised by Mark Wheeller in 1986 using only the words of those most closely involved and affected. Since that time it has become one of the most performed plays ever. This version of the script is revised..and updated with a further tragic incident.

'The play will have an impact on young people or adults. It will provoke discussion. It stimulates and wants you to cry out for immediate social action and resolution.'

*Henry Shankula – Addiction Research Foundation, Toronto*

'The young audience I was sat in was patently out for some whooping Friday night fun... at the end there was a horrid silence.'

*Nick Baker – Times Educational Supplement.*

'A formidable attack on drunken driving.'

*Pru Kitchen – The Scotsman*

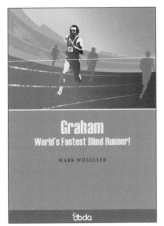

**ISBN 978 1 902843 26 1**

*Cast:* 6 (3m, 3f with doubling).
Can be performed with a cast
of up to around 30. (10m, 8f
& 12 m or f)
*Duration:* 55 minutes
*Suitable for:* ages 13+
or adults!

*Developed from Mark
Wheeller's stage play Race
To Be Seen, written with the
Epping Youth Theatre.*

Available on DVD, the
award winning Oaklands
Youth Theatre production.
*For more information
contact dbda.*

## Graham – World's Fastest Blind Runner! by Mark Wheeller

Written in the same documentary style as Too
Much Punch For Judy, Mark's first version of this
play about Graham Salmon MBE, was awarded
Critics Choice at the Edinburgh Festival Fringe
(1984).

It has recently been re-written, and on it's first
two outings won through to the Final of both the
National Drama Festivals Association in 2007
and the All England Theatre Festival in 2008,
winning different awards at each Festival.

Listed in the Guiness Book of Records as The
Worlds Fastest Blind Runner in 1976 (100m in
11.4 secs) Graham went on to play Golf for the
international visually impaired team for whom he
hit a famous "hole in one" in The British Open!

'I didn't ever need convincing that 'Graham' was an
ideal piece to challenge my group and that it ticked
all the boxes for A-level work, but if I ever needed
justification, then the results have certainly given
it. In the breakdown of the Unit 2 marks i.e. the
performance of 'Graham', all seven candidates were
awarded 100%. It's worth noting that the external
moderator was accompanied that evening by her
senior examiner! Thanks again for the material and
thanks to Graham, such an inspirational person!'
*Mike Fleetwood, Parkside Arts College.*

Selected as an exemplar Unit 2 study text in the
Longman/Pearson 2009 Edexcel GCSE Drama
Teacher and Student book.

# Other plays published by **dbda**

ISBN 978 1 902843 28 5

*Cast:* 2m & 2f
*Duration:* 40 minutes
KS 3 to adult

## Driven to Distraction
## by Danny Sturrock & Mark Wheeller

Driven to Distraction tells the story of how an incident on a bus leads to the death of a fledgling rap artist travelling to a press conference in a nearby vehicle.

The play sees the story from two different perspectives. Firstly the young couple who distract the bus driver... one of whom is the dead girl's estranged brother. Their story is told from the months before the accident to the accident itself.

Zinc, the bus driver's story is also told... from the moment after the accident, showing how it affects his life.

Driven to Distraction is ideal for TIE production, BTEC A Level and GCSE use.

'Felt a real compassion for the characters. Content was focussed and all learning points were reinforced. I would really like all students to be able to see this!'

*Chris Lee, Development Manager, Motorvation Projects Limited.*

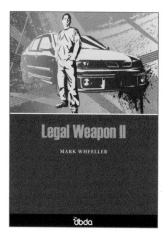

ISBN 978 1 902843 18 6

*Cast:* 32f & 2m with doubling
*Duration:* 60 minutes approx.
KS 3 & 4 and A Level

## Legal Weapon II
## by Mark Wheeller

This is a new "improved" version of the popular Legal Weapon play which is touring schools across the UK.

It is the story of a young man, Andy. His relationship with his girlfriend – and his car – are both flawed, but his speeding causes the loss of a life and the loss of his freedom.

In Legal Weapon II, the story takes an additional twist when Andy realises that the person he's killed is somebody very dear to Jazz, his girlfriend.

**Legal Weapon II promises to be faster, funnier and far more powerful!**

'A gripping storyline. Even the most challenging of our students were held by the drama. This learning experience should be given to each Year 11 as they come through the school.'

*Myrtle Springs Secondary School*

# Other plays published by **dbda**

## Bang Out Of Order
### by Johnny Carrington & Danny Sturrock

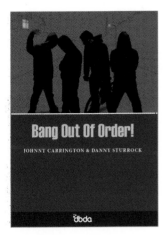

4 friends, 1 secret, 1 chance, 1 life. The play tackles anti-social behaviour head on. This rollercoaster ride will educate, amuse and challenge.

Set on an urban estate, newcomer Ollie has a history of antisocial behaviour and is attempting to reform. His family are forced to move away in an attempt to make a fresh start... but once he is accepted into the local group of youths, things start to go wrong.

The play tackles the sensitive issues using a mixture of comedy, dance, music and multi-media.

'If you are setting out to convey a message, the mixture of naturalism which pulls no punches, stylised movement that moves the action along with wit and mixed media, adds another dimension that certainly grabs the attention of the audience.'

*Fran Morley, Director, Nuffield Theatre Southampton*

ISBN 978 1 902843 21 6

**Cast:** *2m & 2f*
*Suitable for GCSE*
**Duration:** *55 minutes approx.*
**KS 3 & 4**

## Missing Dan Nolan
### by Mark Wheeller

This play, based on the true story of Dan Nolan, a teenage boy who went missing on the night of January 1st 2002, is written in the same documentary style as Too Much Punch for Judy. It has won awards and commendations at every Drama Festival it has entered. It is now, like so many of Mark's other plays, being toured professionally by the Queens Theatre in Hornchurch, Essex.

'Unusual and deeply affecting. Skillfully written... achieves astonishing depth and authenticity... '

*Charles Evans, Adjudicator, Eastleigh Drama Festival*

ISBN 978 1 902843 16 2

**Cast:** *2m & 2f with doubling, or up to 18*
**Duration:** *45-50 minutes*
**KS 3 to adult*

Exemplar text for Unit 2 in the Hodder Education Edexcel Drama for GCSE book (2009 specification) endorsed by Edexcel.

Featured in Mark Wheeller's Drama Schemes book for teachers

# Other plays published by **dbda**

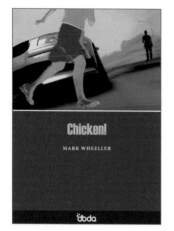

**ISBN 1 902843 19 3**

**Cast:** *34m, 3f & 2m/f or 2m & 2f for GCSE*
**Duration:** *35 minutes approx.*
*KS 3 & 4*

## Chicken!
## by Mark Wheeller

A 'new and improved' version of WHY DID THE CHICKEN CROSS THE ROAD? The play tells the story of two cousins, Tammy and Chris. We are led to believe that something bad will happen to Chris who refuses to wear his cycle helmet. It is, however, Tammy who gets killed on the one morning that the cousins walk to school. Chris remains unwilling to tell anyone of his part in the accident and he has to live with this dreadful secret. One of the main changes is the introduction of Chris filming Tammy's fatal dare on his mobile phone camera.

'We have just been fortunate enough to witness the most superb exhibition of interactive safety education. The performance was quite stunning!'

*Jim Lambert, Head Teacher Sinclair Middle School, Southampton*

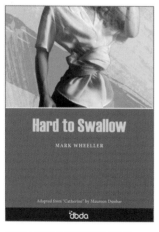

**ISBN 978 1 902843 08 7**

**Cast:** *3f & 2m with doubling, or 6f, 3m & 16*
**Duration:** *70 minutes approx.*
*KS 3 to adult*

## Hard to Swallow
## by Mark Wheeller

This play is an adaptation of Maureen Dunbar's award winning book (and film) **Catherine** which charts her daughter's uneven battle with anorexia and the family's difficulties in coping with the illness.

The play has gone on to be performed all over the world to much acclaim, achieving considerable success in One Act Play Festivals. Its simple narrative style means that it is equally suitable for adult and older youth groups to perform.

'This play reaches moments of almost unbearable intensity... naturalistic scenes flow seamlessly into sequences of highly stylised theatre... such potent theatre!'
*Vera Lustig, The Independent*

'Uncompromising and sensitive... should be compulsory viewing to anyone connected with the education of teenagers.'

*Mick Martin, Times Educational Supplement*

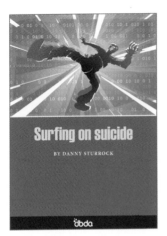

ISBN 978 1 902843 29 2

**Cast:** *2m & 2f*
*Suitable for A' Level to adult*
**Duration:** *55 minutes approx.*
**KS 3 & 4**

## Surfing on Suicide
## by Danny Sturrock

Surfing on Suicide tells the true story of 18 year old Simon Kelly who, after using the internet to obtain detailed information on suicide methods and using suicide chat rooms, tragically took his own life in 2001. He launched a website to act as his suicide note only minutes before he died. This is his story.

'A drama which was is honest, humane, humorous, informative and emotional without being emotive... Fast paced and pitched perfectly... a piece of theatre at its best.'
*Karen Robson - Southern Daily Echo Review*

'In tackling a topic such as suicide there is always the risk of over dramatisation and glorification of the individuals concerned, which could lead other vulnerable youngsters to follow suit.'
*Paul and Hilary Kelly - Simon's Parents*

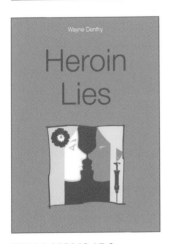

ISBN 1 902843 15 0

**Cast:** *8f, 7m and 2m/f*
**Duration:** *70 minutes approx.*
**KS 3 & 4**

## Heroin Lies
## by Wayne Denfhy

A sensitive, yet disturbing look at drugs and drug dependency, in particular the pressures and influences at play on an ordinary teenage girl. We observe Vicki's gradual and tragic slide towards addiction and also the various degrees of help and hindrance she receives from family and friends.

This is a new, updated edition of Wayne Denfhy's popular play. It is suitable for performance as well as for reading in the class. Included with the playscript is an excellent scheme for follow-up work by Peter Rowlands.

'...a piece of drama that will stimulate and challenge a young cast... Heroin Lies deals with vital issues that affect today's youngsters in a gentle and humane way and, in so doing, gets its message across without the instant rejection that can meet other approaches.'
*Pete Sanpher, Head of Drama, Norfolk*

# Other plays published by **dbda**

## Gagging for it
## by Danny Sturrock

Summer is here, A-levels are over and a group of 6 friends embark on a holiday to Ibiza! What would their holiday bring? Would Chris finally pluck up the courage to ask out Teresa? Would Jay drink himself into oblivion? Would Bianca spend the entire holiday flirting with the Spanish barmen – more than likely! …or would their experiments with drugs bring their hedonistic worlds crashing down around them!?

Comedy, dance, music and choreography are the keys to this production. The pace is breakneck and hilarious, but once the party's over, it hits you!

'Really funny… laugh out loud funny. Inspired outstanding performances from the six Year 11s who went on to exceed our expectations by a long way in their GCSEs achieving A or A*. It proved to be a firm favourite with our KS3/4 audience.'

*Mark Wheeller*

**ISBN 1 902843 17 7**

*Cast:* 33f, 3m &3m/f or 3m & 3f for GCSE using suggested cuts
*Duration: 55 minutes approx.*
**KS 3 & 4.**

## The Gate Escape by Mark Wheeller

The story of two truants. Corey is 'addicted' to bunking school. Chalkie views himself as a casual truant "no problem!" While truanting with some friends, the pair are greeted by a surreal 'Big Brother' figure who sets them a task. The loser will be in for some dramatic 'Big Bother'… Who will lose?… What will this 'bother' be?

The play has toured professionally throughout the south of England to great acclaim.

'A lively dramatic style and innovative structure with dynamic and contemporary dialogue. It is written in a way to guarantee that the audience will feel fully involved and enthralled by the main characters.'

*Professor Ken Reid, Author of Tackling Truancy in Schools*

'Theatrically interesting… excellent basis for active discussion of issues and dramatic style with reluctant GCSE students'

*Ali Warren (National Drama)*